Show Tunes

11.95

Wise Publications
London/New York/Paris/Sydney/
Copenhagen/Madrid

Exclusive Distributors:
Music Sales Limited
8/9 Frith Street, London W1V 5TZ, England.
Music Sales Pty Limited
120 Rothschild Avenue, Rosebery, NSW 2018, Australia.

This book © Copyright 1993 by
Wise Publications
Order No.AM91039
ISBN 0-7119-3363-4

Music processed by Interactive Sciences Limited, Gloucester
Book design by Hutton Staniford
Music arranged by Stephen Duro
Compiled by Peter Evans

Photographs courtesy of:
London Features International

Music Sales' complete catalogue lists thousands of titles and is free from your local music shop,
or direct from Music Sales Limited. Please send a cheque/postal order for £1.50 for postage to:
Music Sales Limited, Newmarket Road, Bury St. Edmunds, Suffolk IP33 3YB.

Your Guarantee of Quality:

As publishers, we strive to produce every book to the highest commercial standards.

All the music has been freshly engraved and the book has been carefully designed to minimise
awkward page turns and to make playing from it a real pleasure.

Particular care has been given to specifying acid-free, neutral-sized paper which has not been
chlorine bleached but produced with special regard for the environment. Throughout, the printing
and binding have been planned to ensure a sturdy, attractive publication which should give
years of enjoyment.

If your copy fails to meet our high standards, please inform us and we will gladly replace it.

Printed in the United Kingdom by
Halstan & Co Limited, Amersham, Buckinghamshire.

Another Suitcase In Another Hall (Evita)   4

Big Spender (Sweet Charity)   6

Don't Cry For Me Argentina (Evita)   9

Don't Let The Sun Catch You Crying (Five Guys Named Moe)   12

I Dreamed A Dream (Les Misérables)   15

Is You Is, Or Is You Ain't (Ma' Baby) (Five Guys Named Moe)   18

Luck Be A Lady (Guys And Dolls)   28

Maria (West Side Story)   20

Marilyn Monroe (Blood Brothers)   22

Now That I've Seen Her (Miss Saigon)   24

Ol' Man River (Show Boat)   31

On My Own (Les Misérables)   34

Pick A Pocket Or Two (Oliver!)   37

Send In The Clowns (A Little Night Music)   40

Tell Me It's Not True (Blood Brothers)   43

Tonight (West Side Story)   46

Another Suitcase In Another Hall

Music by Andrew Lloyd Webber, Lyrics by Tim Rice

Slow

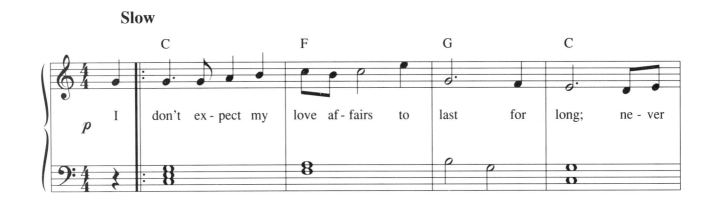

I don't ex-pect my love af-fairs to last for long; ne-ver

fool my - self that my dreams_____ will come true.

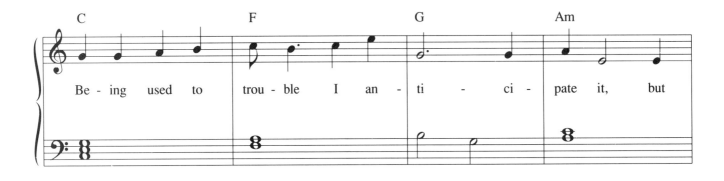

Be - ing used to trou - ble I an - ti - ci - pate it, but

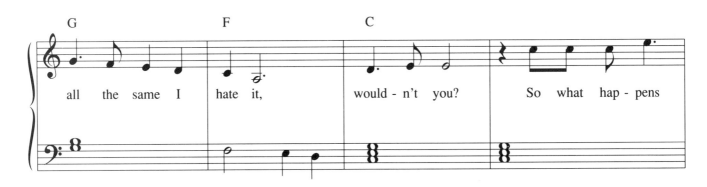

all the same I hate it, would - n't you? So what hap - pens

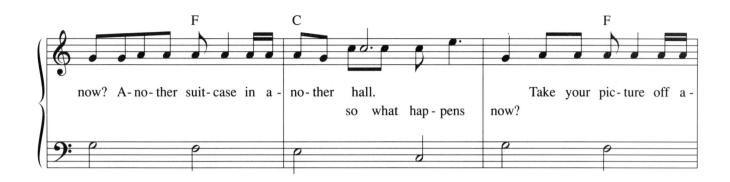

now? A-no-ther suit-case in a-no-ther hall.
so what hap-pens
Take your pic-ture off a-
now?

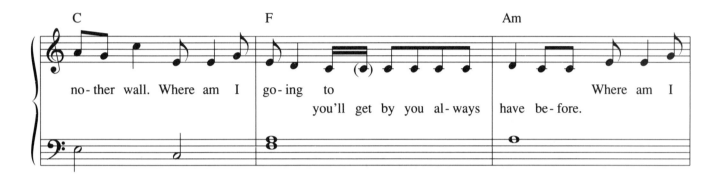

no-ther wall. Where am I go-ing to
you'll get by you al-ways have be-fore.
Where am I

1,2.
go - ing to?

3.
go - ing to? Don't ask an - y - more.

2. Time and time again I've said that I don't care;
   That I'm immune to gloom, that I'm hard through and through.
   But every time it matters all my words desert me;
   So anyone can hurt me – and they do.
       So what happens now? *etc.*

3. Call in three months' time and I'll be fine I know;
   Well maybe not that fine, but I'll survive anyhow;
   I won't recall the names and places of this sad occasion;
   But that's no consolation, here and now.
       So what happens now? *etc.*

Big Spender

Words by Dorothy Fields, Music by Cy Coleman

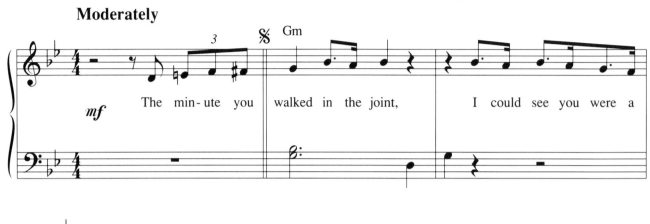

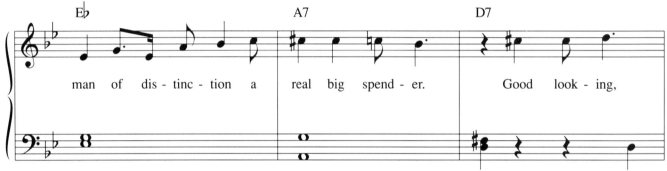

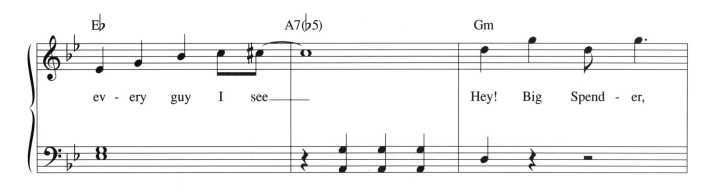

ev - ery guy I see___ Hey! Big Spend - er,

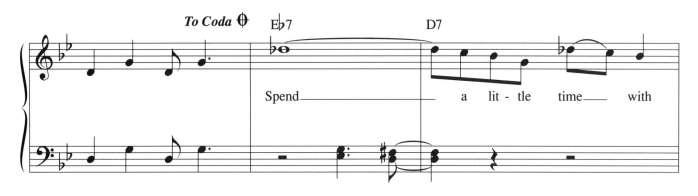

Spend_____ a lit - tle time___ with

me.

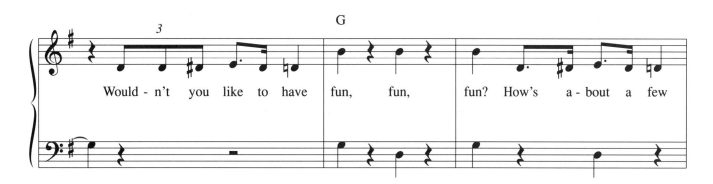

Would - n't you like to have fun, fun, fun? How's a - bout a few

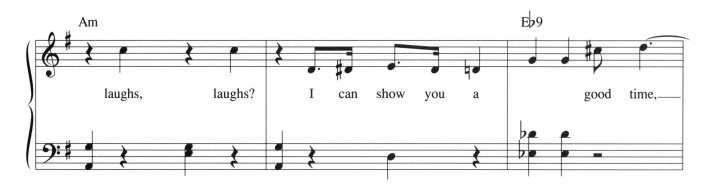

laughs, laughs? I can show you a good time,___

Don't Cry For Me Argentina

Music by Andrew Lloyd Webber, Lyrics by Tim Rice

Slowly

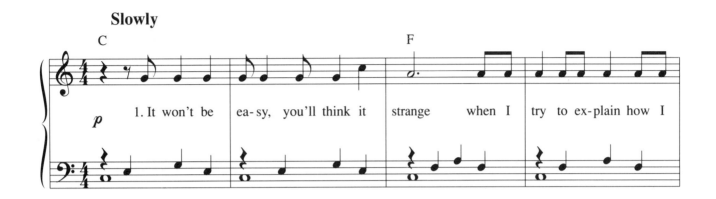

1. It won't be ea-sy, you'll think it strange when I try to ex-plain how I

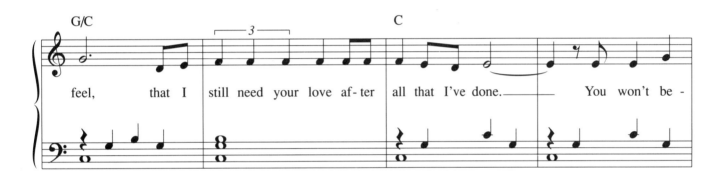

feel, that I still need your love af-ter all that I've done.___ You won't be -

lieve me. All you will see is a girl you once knew, al -

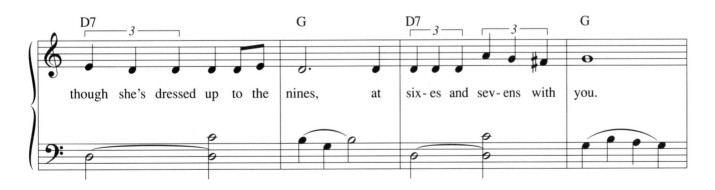

though she's dressed up to the nines, at six-es and sev-ens with you.

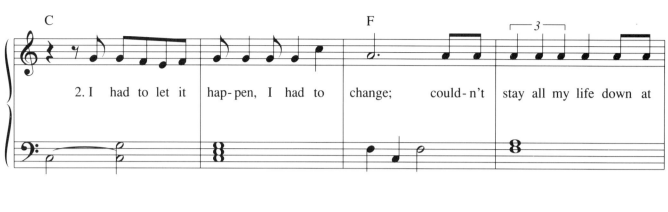

2. I had to let it hap-pen, I had to change; could-n't stay all my life down at

heel. Look-ing out of the win-dow, stay-ing out of the sun. So I chose

free-dom. Run-ning a-round try-ing ev-ery-thing new, but no-thing im-pressed me at

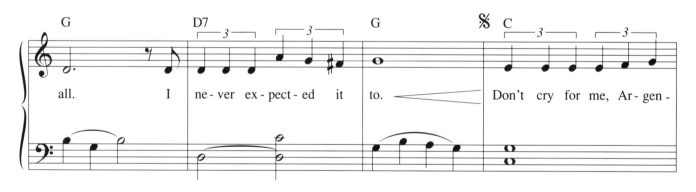

all. I ne-ver ex-pect-ed it to. Don't cry for me, Ar-gen-

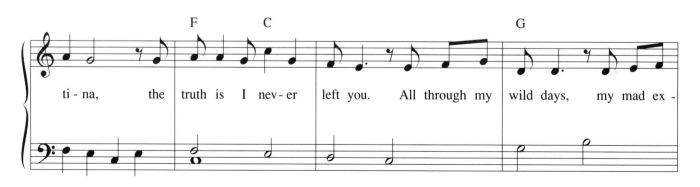

ti-na, the truth is I nev-er left you. All through my wild days, my mad ex-

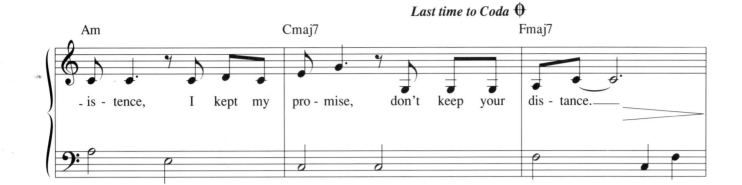

-is - tence, I kept my pro - mise, don't keep your dis - tance.

Have I said too much? There's no - thing more I can think of to say to you.

But all you have to do is look at me to know that ev - ery

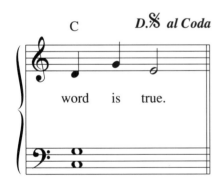

word is true.

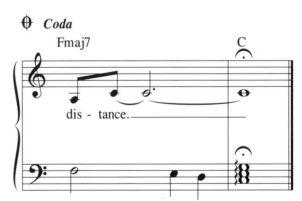

dis - tance.

3. And as for fortune and as for fame,
   I never invited them in.
   Though it seemed to the world they were all I desired.
   They are illusions.
   They are not the solution they promised to be,
   The answer was here all the time.
   I love you and hope you love me.

Don't Let The Sun Catch You Crying

Words & Music by Joe Greene

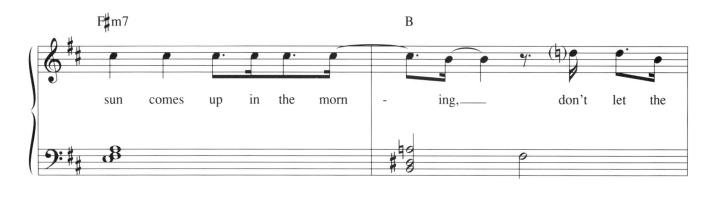

F#m7   B

sun comes up in the morn - ing,___ don't let the

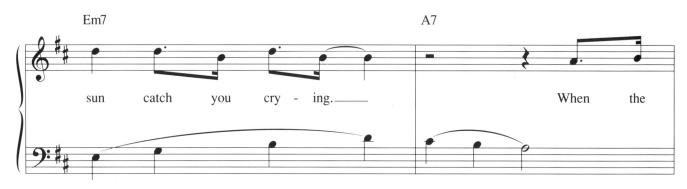

Em7   A7

sun catch you cry - ing.___ When the

F#m (♭5)   B7

moon goes down in the dawn - ing,___ don't let the

Em7   A7

sun catch you cry - ing, 'cause ba - by don't want___ you no more.___

D   G   G#dim   D⁹₆

I Dreamed A Dream

Music by Claude-Michel Schönberg, Lyrics by Herbert Kretzmer
Original Text by Alain Boublil & Jean-Marc Natel

-ge - ther.___ But there are dreams which can - not be

and there are storms we can - not wea - ther.___

I had a dream my life would be so diff - 'rent from this hell I'm

liv - ing___ so diff-'rent now from what it seemed. Now life has killed the dream I

dreamed.

Is You Is, Or Is You Ain't (Ma' Baby)

Words & Music by Billy Austin & Louis Jordan

Maria

Music by Leonard Bernstein, Lyrics by Stephen Sondheim

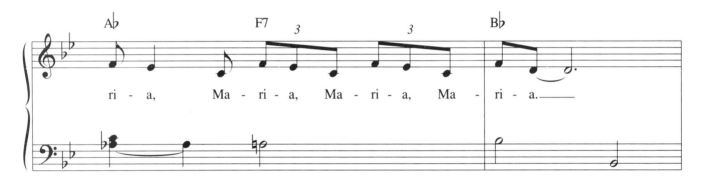

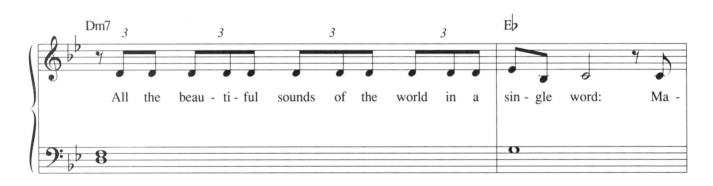

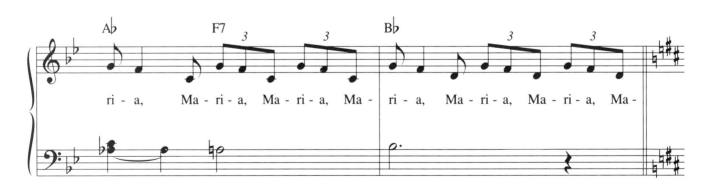

-ri- a,— I've just met a girl named Ma - ri- a.— And sud-den-ly that name will

ne- ver be the same to me. Ma - ri- a,— I've just kissed a girl named Ma -

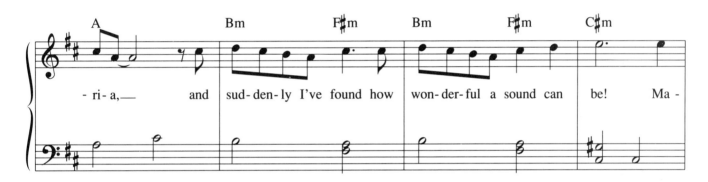

- ri- a,— and sud-den-ly I've found how won-der-ful a sound can be! Ma -

- ri- a,— say it loud and there's mu- sic play-ing.— Say it soft and it's al-most like

pray- ing.— Ma - ri- a,— I'll ne- ver stop say-ing "Ma - ri- a."—

pp

Marilyn Monroe

Words & Music by Willy Russell

Now That I've Seen Her

Music by Claude-Michel Schönberg, Lyrics by Richard Maltby Jnr. & Alain Boublil

Moderately

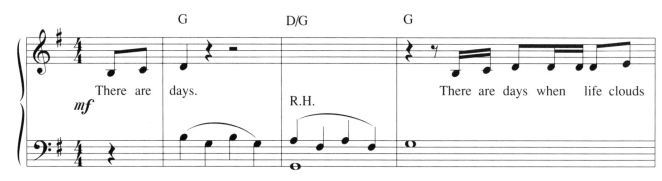

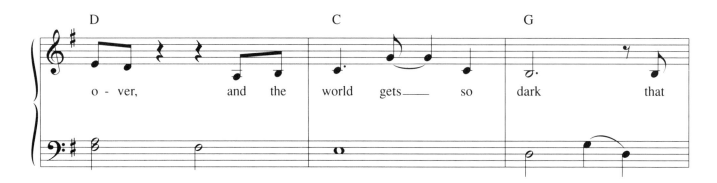

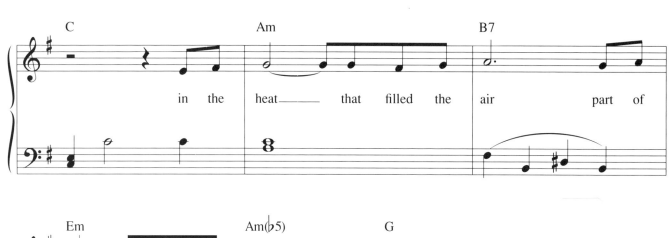

in the heat____ that filled the air part of

him____ still lin - gers there. I know what pain her life to -

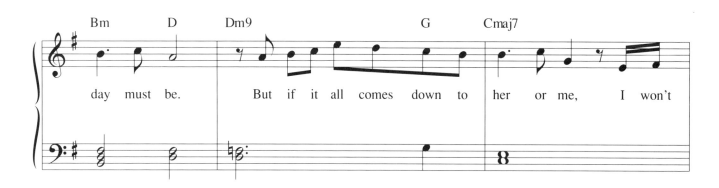

day must be. But if it all comes down to her or me, I won't

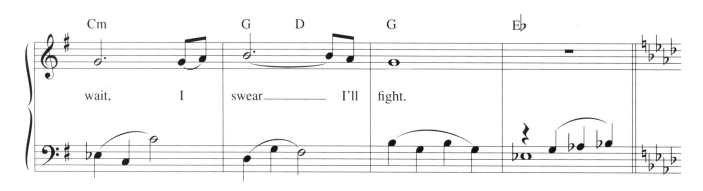

wait, I swear____ I'll fight.

Now that____ I've seen her____ she's more than____ a

Luck Be A Lady

Words & Music by Frank Loesser

Moderately

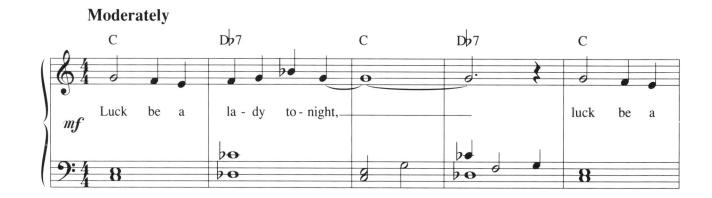

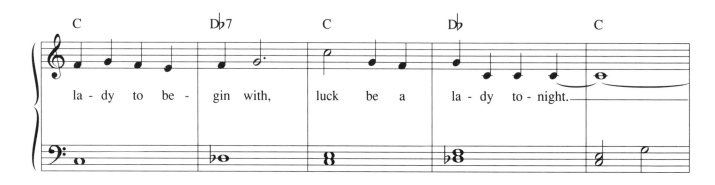

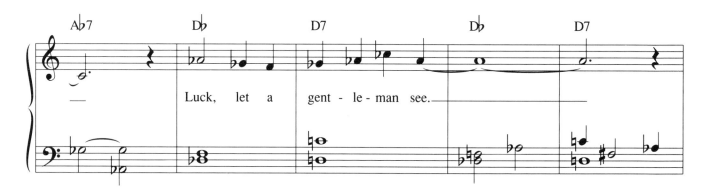

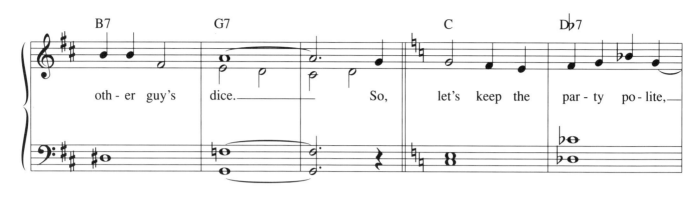

oth - er guy's dice._____ So, let's keep the par - ty po - lite,_____

_____ Ne - ver get out of my sight._____

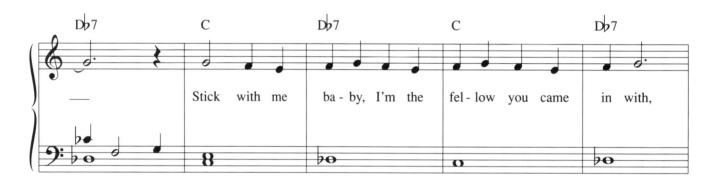

_____ Stick with me ba - by, I'm the fel - low you came in with,

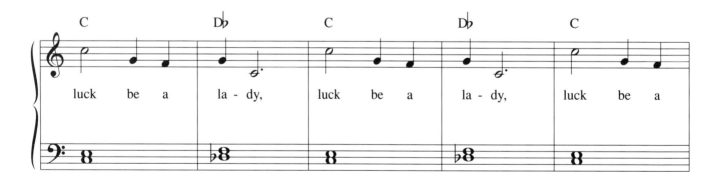

luck be a la - dy, luck be a la - dy, luck be a

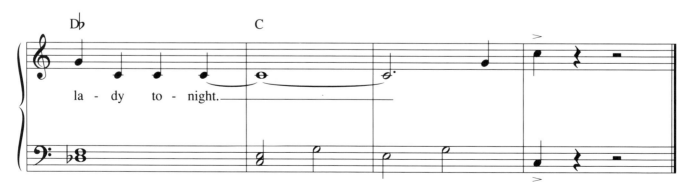

la - dy to - night._____

Ol' Man River

Music by Jerome Kern, Words by Oscar Hammerstein II

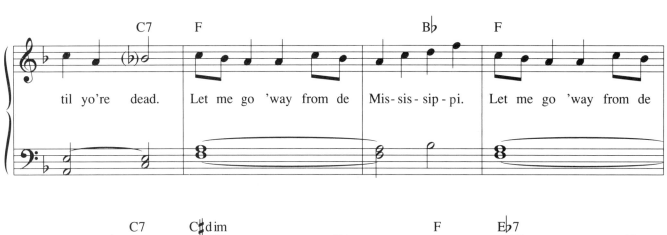

til yo're dead. Let me go 'way from de Mis-sis-sip-pi. Let me go 'way from de

white man boss, Show me dat stream called de riv-er Jor-dan, dat's de ol' stream dat I

long to cross.⎯ Ol' man ri-ver, dat ol' man ri-ver, he

must know sump-in'; but don't say noth-in'; he jus' keeps roll-in'; he keeps on roll-in' a-

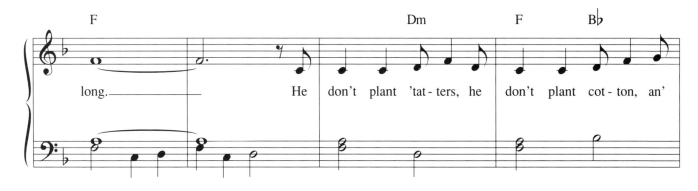

long.⎯ He don't plant 'tat-ters, he don't plant cot-ton, an'

On My Own

Music by Claude-Michel Schönberg, Lyrics by Herbert Kretzmer
Original Text by Alain Boublil & Jean-Marc Natel

Moderately

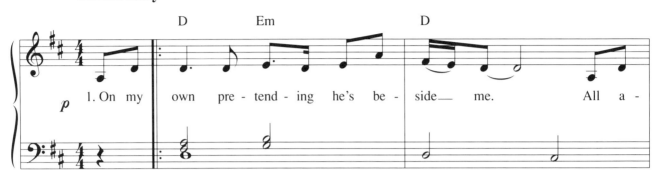

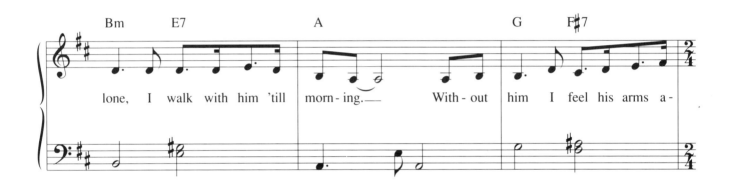

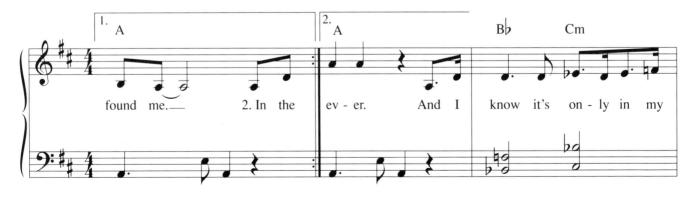

2. In the rain, the pavement shines like silver.
   All the lights are misty in the river.
   In the darkness, the trees are full of starlight.
   And all I see is him and me forever and forever.

Pick A Pocket Or Two

Words & Music by Lionel Bart

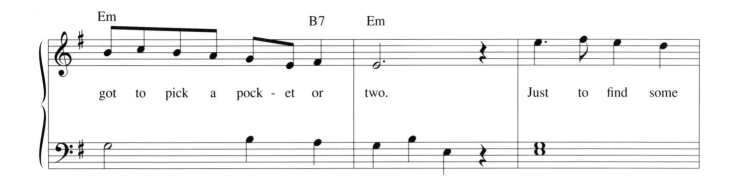

got to pick a pock - et or two. Just to find some

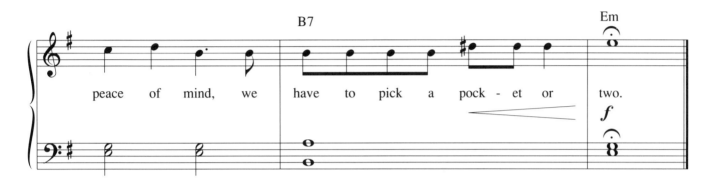

peace of mind, we have to pick a pock - et or two.

2. Why should we break our backs, stupidly paying tax?
   Better get some untaxed income: better pick a pocket or two.
   You've got to pick a pocket or two, boys,
   You've got to pick a pocket or two!
   Why should we all break our backs? Better pick a pocket or two.

3. Robin Hood, what a crook! Gave away what he took.
   Charity's fine, subscribe to mine! Get out and pick a pocket or two.
   You've got to pick a pocket or two, boys,
   You've got to pick a pocket or two.
   Robin Hood was far too good, get out and pick a pocket or two.

4. Take a tip from Bill Sikes – he can whip what he likes,
   I recall he started small, he had to pick a pocket or two.
   You've got to pick a pocket or two, boys,
   You've got to pick a pocket or two.
   We can be like old Bill Sikes, if we pick a pocket or two.

Send In The Clowns

Words & Music by Stephen Sondheim

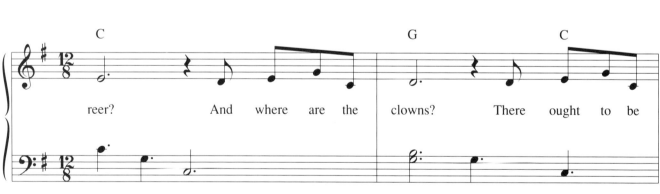

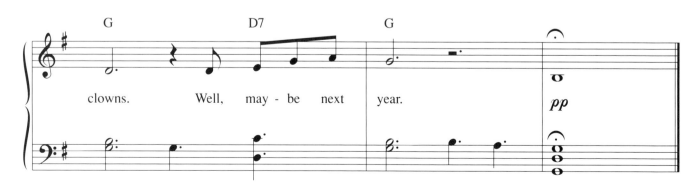

Tell Me It's Not True

Words & Music by Willy Russell

Tonight

Music by Leonard Bernstein, Lyrics by Stephen Sondheim

Moderately